MUSHROOMS & TOADSTOOLS
HOW TO FIND AND IDENTIFY THEM

With an introduction by Uberto Tosco and Annalaura Fanelli

**LONDON
ORBIS BOOKS**

Contents

Acknowledgments are due to the following for photographs used in this volume: Archivio B., M. Bavestrelli, E. Dulevant, R. Longo, A. Margiocco, G. Mazza, A. Sella, G. Tomsich, S. Viola

Translated from the Italian of Uberto Tosco and Annalaura Fanelli

Although mushrooms and other fungi have been the subject of long and detailed studies, they still retain a certain mystery. These curious plants that flourish in woods, on barks, in meadows and fields, constitute an inexhaustible subject. And for those who eat or would like to eat wild mushrooms, an accurate description of different fungi is essential. A cursory knowledge of such characteristics as the colour of the caps, or the transformation that takes place when the skin is broken or exposed to the air, is not sufficient.

For this reason alone, one more book on the subject is always welcome. A new illustration, an account of a specific characteristic – perhaps one underestimated by other authors – can illuminate a concept or help to identify, with more assurance, a species or one of its varieties.

This is not a scientific work. It has no other aim than to help the collector or the observer with his quest. But it should be stressed that the interest of fungi is not limited to the matter of whether they are delicious or deadly. They occupy a unique and fascinating place in nature, and for many they are of considerable esthetic value.

Mycology, the study of fungi, provides an absorbing subject but, even for those whose interest in the matter is purely gastronomic, this book will prove rewarding. It will enable the reader to enlarge, little by little, the range of species on which he dines, although it must be remembered that, if knowledge breeds confidence, it should also breed respect. It is true that there are very few poisonous fungi, and by no means all of these cause deadly or even particularly serious poisoning. It is also true that several of the poisonous species are easily avoided because they have a disagreeable taste and smell, and a tough, woody consistency. But this is not always the case, and even the really edible, delicious and completely inoffensive species can become dangerous with deterioration, like any other food substance. Moreover, some edible species become poisonous when in an advanced stage of development.

The following pages contain a few elementary notions on the morphology, birth and classification of fungi. A series of colour photographs draws attention to all the characteristics that make possible the certain identification of each species. In selecting these illustrations, particular stress has been laid on those characteristics that make it possible to distinguish between species which appear deceptively similar.

Uberto Tosco and Annalaura Fanelli

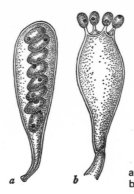

a) Cross-section of an ascus, showing ascospores.
b) Basidium and basidiospores.

The 'Third Kingdom'

In common parlance the term 'mushroom' is applied to an edible fungus and the term 'toadstool' to an inedible or poisonous fungus. In both cases we are referring to 'macro-fungi', and it should be pointed out that 'micro-fungi' fulfill a function in nature that is even more important in the life of man. It is to this microscopic universe that belong yeasts and ferments, parasites which ravage crops, moulds which decay foodstuffs, paper and hide, countless agents of disease but also numerous antibiotics. However, these micro-fungi are not the subject of this book, and the term 'fungi' will be used as a synonym for 'mushrooms and toadstools'.

Such a vast group, containing about 100,000 species, offers so wide a variety of structures, that their systematic classification and the determination of their phylogenic or evolutionary history have given rise to many difficulties.

Fungi are traditionally considered as plants, but are really quite distinct: they are therefore known sometimes as the 'Third Kingdom'. They have no chlorophyll, roots, stems or leaves and hardly resemble any true plant. They also have several features found in the animal kingdom, besides numerous features characteristic of themselves alone.

With the exception of the more primitive forms, which are unicellular, the typical fungi are composed of a more or less compact tangle of fine filaments, which is called a mycelium. These filaments, the hyphae, branch out into the materials from which they derive their nutrition.

The absence of chlorophyll prevents fungi from exploiting directly the carbon contained in the atmosphere, as green plants generally do. In order to live and grow, therefore, the mycelium must procure for itself organic substances produced by other organisms.

One way by which fungi may be classified is their mode of nutrition. First there are the simple saprophytes, which live on dead or decomposing organic matter such as manure, dry leaves and humus. Parasites, on the other hand, consume living organisms, either animal or vegetable. Symbionts, at the top of the scale, exist in association with another species, to the advantages of both. Lichen, which is composed of algae and fungi, provides a good example of symbiosis.

Very significant examples of symbiosis can also be found among the macro-fungi. Fungi such as the amanitas, russulas, truffles, cortinarii, tricholomas and above all boleti, depend for their existence upon the presence of a certain kind of tree, shrub or bush: oaks, poplars and willows for truffles; beach and chestnut, as a rule, for boleti; the Scotch fir for *Boletus bovinus*, and so on. Such fungi are not true parasites. In each case the superior plants draws some food from the nutritive-absorptive connection between mycelium and root (a relationship known as mycorrhiza).

Superior fungi and their role in nature

Since fungi generally lack autonomous life, they exist without many of the functions and hence without many of the organs possessed by other, more complicated, plants. However, like all other living things they have their biological cycle, the supreme aim of which is the preservation of their own species.

The mycelium, in addition to reproducing by natural or artificial fragmentation, can reproduce itself under specific conditions. In fact, there is a great variety of reproductive structures, and on these, rather than their nutrition, the classification of fungi has been established.

It is necessary for this account to limit discussion to what are termed 'superior fungi', that is to say the fungi people collect and cultivate. What we collect is really the 'fruit' (carpophore) of a fungus rather than the fungus itself; the true fungus, the mycelium, lies under the ground. And it is the carpophore that contains the spores (roughly corresponding to the seeds of other plants) which are the reproductive agents of the fungi.

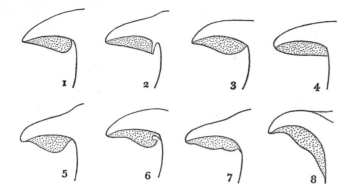

Different types of gills: 1) free; 2) separated from the stem by a collar; 3) separated or near the stem; 4) adnate; 5) sinuate; 6) forked or sinuate and margined; 7) decurrent, forming a tooth; 8) strongly decurrent.

Ascomycetes and Basidiomycetes

The prime function of the carpophore is to provide for the dissemination of the spores. The spores are microscopic structures produced in vast quantities and in a great diversity of forms, colours and dimensions according to the different types and species.

The superior fungi are divided into two quite distinct classes according to the formation of the spores: *Ascomycetes* and *Basidiomycetes*. With the former, the spores are contained in fours or eights in the cavity of very elongated cells called asci; the latter are equipped with completely different cells, the basidia, which are tubular and produce their spores outside the cells on two or four small stalks (sterigmata).

The asci, like the basidia, occupy well-defined zones of the fruiting body, where they are mixed with sterile cells (paraphyses) to form a fertile bed, the hymenium.

In the larger forms of the *Ascomycetes*, to which, for example, belong pezizas, morels and helvellas, this bed appears as a microscopic veil usually turned upwards and covering the fruiting body in the form of an open cup or 'mitre'.

Truffles constitute the only exception. In appearance, these underground fungi imitate tubers: the hymenium fills the internal part, the gleba, decorating it with characteristic veins.

Among the *Basidiomycetes* there are two main groups: 'Gasteromycetes' (for example puff-balls) which are fungi whose spore-producing tissue constitutes entirely the internal part of the fungus; and 'Hymenomycetes', which make up the larger group of the edible fungi, and where the hymenium is entirely external, adapted to the highest degree of complexity.

The distribution and structure of this hymenium varies from one group of fungi to another. There are two main types: fungi with caps have the hymenium underneath, distributed on gills (*Agaricaceae*), in tubes (*Boletaceae* or *Polyporaceae*), or on spines (*Hydnaceae*); whereas in *Clavaria* and *Morchella*, for example, it is exposed on folds or at the tips of branches.

A guide to identification

From the immense variety of forms described, some can be chosen, which, because of their characteristic external structures, illustrate the most common kinds.

For example, in the case of *Amanita caesarea*, it is known that during the first stages of its development a white membrane, the volva, protects it like an egg shell. Yet if the young fungus is divided into sections, the adult fungus, already formed, can be seen. This will emerge by tearing the wrapping and leaving a volva at the base of the foot.

When the fungus is completely developed, the following parts can easily be distinguished: a 'stalk', and generally an enlarged part in the form of an umbrella, the 'cap'. Below this cap radiate numerous 'gills' covered by the fertile hymenium; the stalk is adorned, just below the cap, with a small membranous and drooping skirt, the 'ring', which is nothing more than the protective membrane of the gills. This membrane, which is called a partial veil, detaches itself when the cap opens. This fungus is representative of one of the most evolved families and one of those most distinguished by their structures.

The *Agaricaceae* include both the most tasty and the most dangerous species; for example, the edible mushroom and the Death Cap, *Amanita phalloides*.

Related to the Death Cap is the Spring Amanita (*Amanita verna*) and *A. virosa*: they are equally poisonous. They are both white, but their caps turn yellow when scarcely at the adult stage.

Another group of amanitas has scales on the cap. These are the remains of the volva, which has broken into pieces as the cap has developed. It is not difficult to distinguish species of these fungi from the colour of their cap. The cap of the Fly Agaric (*Amanita muscaria*) is a

Schematic drawing illustrating spore dispersal, the development of the mycelium and the propagation of the fungi.

beautiful golden red. The Panther Cap (*A. pantherina*) is brown or grey brown, and bristles with pyramidal scales. Like the Fly Agaric, it is very poisonous. *A. vaginata*, commonly called 'grisette', is non-poisonous and differs from the others in that it does not have a ring.

Akin to the amanitas is the *Lepiota* genus, to which belongs the 'parasol' mushroom (*L. procera*). *Volvaria* species, in which quite a large volva encircles the base of the foot, are members of the same family. These have no ring and, moreover, their gills and spores are pink. On the contrary, the very mobile ring is always present in *Lepiota*: they have gills which are sometimes white, and sometimes barely pink, such as those of *L. naucina*, an edible species.

It is well to remember that field mushrooms (*Agaricus* or *Psalliota* family) also have a ring and no volva. Thanks to this characteristic, and to the fact that their gills, once they have reached maturity, take on a deep red colour, they can be distinguished from the amanitas like *A. verna* or *A. virosa*, which are entirely white or at most have a slightly mottled stem. Moreover, the field mushrooms can be distinguished from *Entoloma sinuatus* (poisonous), as the latter has no ring. However, it is still necessary to make a distinction between different field mushrooms as, for example, a species like *Agaricus xanthoderma* is not edible. It may be recognised by its less stocky appearance and its much more slender stem, and above all by the very clear yellowing of its cap immediately after it is rubbed.

A ring is also evident in *Armillaria*, a genus that includes the honey-coloured *Armillaria mellea*, which appears in groups, like *Hypholoma*. The latter, once they are adult, do not show any trace of a ring, nor the original lining of the gills.

Cortinarius species often have the base of their stem swollen in the form of a bulb or top. Moreover, these fungi are recognisable by the colour of their gills (and their spores), a variable bright rusty ochre often verging on deep red. They also have a characteristic 'cortine' (a silky web) below the cap.

Among the *Cortinarius* species, *Cortinarius praestans* is edible, and often reaches considerable dimensions. Its cap is russet brown, but the gills are slightly purplish blue, and the bulbous stem is mottled and scaly.

In most fungi with gills, however, characteristic parts like the volva, the ring and the cortine are not present when the fungus is young. Nevertheless, it is possible to make distinctions in this vast range of families and species, according to the different means by which the gills in the young fungus are protected. In the young lacteous mushrooms, for example, the edge of the cap is rolled in to protect the gills. Then the cap enlarges, but at the adult stage the edge stills remains slightly involute.

The large groups *Tricholoma* and *Clitocybe* – many species of which bear a confusing resemblance to one another – are without all the characteristics mentioned above. Among the important *Tricholomae* is the St George's Mushroom (*Tricholoma georgii*). It is a small spring mushroom with a colour ranging from a whitish shade to a pale ochre; its cap is thick and its gills very close. This mushroom is characterised by a strong smell of wheat flour, which not everyone appreciates, although it is certainly edible.

Other tricholomas have this smell of flour, but are less frequently eaten. *Tricholoma albobrunnea* has a russet-brown cap and lower stem, with a whitish and floury upper stem.

Tricholoma equestre and *T. sulfurum* are both yellow, but while the first is edible, the second is not because of its strong smell. *T. rutilans* is yellow and its cap and stem are heavily speckled with red. It is edible and is gathered in pine woods during the autumn; the flesh is odourless and agreeable to the taste.

The *Tricholomae*, however, are not without poisonous members. *T. tigrinum* (or *T. pardinum*), *T. murinaceum* and *T. virgatum* belong to this category, and the first mentioned is without any doubt the most dangerous of the whole group. It can be identified by its convex cap, which is crowned with a nipple and decorated with small grey-brown scales, and by its greyish-white gills.

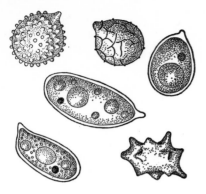

Different types of spores.

Fungus of the amanita type: the base of the stem is enfolded in a volva, and carries a ring on its upper part. The cap is decorated with scales.

However, it can be confused with *T. terreum* which is edible. The latter is smaller, its stem is fragile, cylindrical and stuffed with pith, and its cap is garnished with small, extremely fine, fibrous scale.

The possibility of confusion between the field mushrooms and *Entoloma sinuatus* has already been mentioned, and it has been pointed out that the latter is distinguished by its lack of a ring. This *Entoloma*, like the other species of the same genus, has gills of a more or less intense pink, never deep red like the field mushrooms. The skin is brittle, thin at the edges and smells of flour. It is poisonous, unlike the other species of this family such as *E. clypeatus*, a slender mushroom which often grows in clusters and is a symbiont with cultivated plants (pear or apple trees). Moreover, other members of this family are suspect, for example *E. nidorosus*. Consequently, great care and attention must be exercised to avoid dangerous mistakes that can be made even by those who have some knowledge of fungi.

Rhodopaxillus is so closely linked with the *Tricholomae* that one of its species, *Rhodopaxillus nudus*, has *Tricholoma nudum* as an alternative name. It is a beautiful fungus of an unusually bright violet colour; in the adult stage the cap turns ochre, whereas the gills keep their purplish–blue tones. Despite this strange colouring, this *Rhodopaxillus* is edible.

The rhodopaxilli are not the only wood mushrooms to have fantastic colours. *Cortinarius violaceus* is a beautiful species recognisable by its deep violet colour, even brighter than that of *Rhodopaxillus*; however, when the spores reach maturity, the gills take on an orangy-rust tinge. Among the more unlikely fungi colours is the bluish green of *Clitocybe odora*, a very edible mushroom which emits an agreeable smell of aniseed.

All the fungi described above show the characteristic of a convex cap crowned with a very obvious nipple. Many fungi have a cap which is flat or concave, sometimes even having the shape of a funnel. The three main types, *Paxillus*, *Russula* and *Lactarius* all grow in woods.

The *Paxillus* genus, found mainly in poplar groves, is represented by *Paxillus involutus*, so named because the cap rolls over the gills – a feature already noted. This fungus is also called 'brown chanterelle' because of its chestnut-brown colour, which becomes deeper and more livid when touched. In fact, its form is akin to that of the real chanterelle, *Cantharellus cibarius*, which is golden in colour and fairly common.

The genus *Russula* has always been difficult to classify systematically because of the great variety of species. These fungi, which can reach considerable proportions, are characterised by a convex cap, which with maturity becomes concave or funnel-shaped. The stem is rather short and the colours vary widely, not only within the genus but also within the species themselves. *Russula cyanoxantha*, for example, can have a deep violet or purple cap, and also a deep green one. However, once they have reached the adult stage, both types become dull, especially if they have been subjected to rain. Their gills and stems are invariably white. *R. virescens* (verdigris), which is very edible, is stockier than *R. cyanoxantha*, and has a cap which is dry in appearance. It is pale ochre in colour.

However, the most common characteristic of the russulas is a red cap, and the species so marked are numerous: perhaps as many as a hundred. The distinction between such species is not easy, except where secondary features intervene. The gills may vary in colour from white to a more or less constant yellow; the delicately shaded stem is sometimes pink, sometimes violet; the surfaces of the spores – seen in a microscope – seem to bristle with long spines, either reticulated, finely sculptured or streaked.

Among the russulas, *Russula emetica* must be noted because it is poisonous, and must not be confused with *R. lepida*, which is edible, or with other species such as *R. fragilis*. Generally, *R. fragilis* can be distinguished from *R. emetica* by its larger size and by the jagged edge of the gills.

The very distinctive and numerous *Lactarius* family is characterised by the milk which flows from their skin

Fungus of the entoloma and tricholoma type: the lower part of the cap is trimmed with gills and the stem has neither volva nor ring.

Fungus of the lactarius type: the cap is concave or the gills decurrent, and drops of milk seep from its skin.

when it is broken. *Lactarius deliciosus* is a rather stocky fungus with a cap that is funnel-shaped when completely developed; this cap is marked with reddish concentric circles on an orangy-ochre background, and its gills, when touched, show pale green traces. Its uniqueness stems from the fact that an orangy-red milk flows as soon as the skin is broken.

A white milk is the universal characteristic of the white lactarii, such as *Lactarius piperatus*. This fungus is of considerable size and is further distinguished by its very close gills. The less dense gills observed in *L. vellereus* (which has a slightly velvety cap) are pink in *L. controversus* and ochre in *L. scrobiculatus*; the latter is characterised by the hollows which decorate its stem and by its white milk, which becomes yellowish on contact with the air. *L. chrysorhoeus* is small in size, pale pink in colour and has a speckled cap; its colourless milk becomes sulphur yellow when exposed to air. *L. torminosus*, nicknamed the Woolly Milk Cap, is often confused with *L. deliciosus*, but it can be distinguished by its white milk and the felt-like appearance of the cap veil.

Until now we have been speaking of 'fungi with gills', and as we have chosen the genus *Amanita* to describe the *Agaricaceae* in general, we shall choose the genus *Boletus* for the fungi whose fleshy and solid cap has underneath it a spongy mass of tubes which open to the atmosphere.

Boleti occur in an extremely wide variety of forms within a large range of species. Some are stocky, others slender; some always have a white, others a yellow skin, while some have a white skin which becomes blue green when broken. The latter belong to the fungi which change colour, which include the Satanic Boletus (*Boletus satanas*), the Lurid Boletus (*B. luridus*), the one with a beautiful stem (*B. calopus*), and many more. The Satanic Boletus is so named because it is poisonous, while the Lurid Boletus, frequently considered edible, has been said to produce unpleasant symptoms.

In the absence of more precise mycological knowledge, it is advisable to avoid boleti if the flesh changes colour when broken. The two rough-stemmed boleti are

exceptions to this rule: the first, (*Boletus scaber*), has a brown-grey cap and the other (*B. rufus*) is more stocky and has a brick-red cap. These two fungi, which are absolutely harmless, have a stem with white flesh which, when cut, becomes greyish or blue or even purplish blue at the base; the entire flesh of these fungi becomes blackish when cooked.

In the majority of boleti the colour of the pores and of the hairs which decorate the stem makes it relatively simple to distinguish the edible from the inedible. They are red in the Satanic Boletus and in the Lurid Boletus, whereas they are white or pale yellow in the edible fungi (the pores can even become yellow, verging on green).

Three species come under the heading of edible fungi: the Cep (*Boletus edulis*) with an ochre-chestnut cap, *B. aerus* with a blackish-brown cap, and finally *B. pinicola*, which has a beautiful copper-red cap. All three make excellent eating, either fresh or dried.

At one time the family *Polyporaceae*, characterised by the presence of pores underneath the cap, was frequently confused with the boleti. The real polypori, however, do not have a central stem, as do the boleti. In fact, many polypori are sessile, that is to say their cap – if it is still appropriate to refer to it as a cap – is flush with the bark of the tree trunks on which they grow.

Some of these fungi appear in the shape of a bracket, a tongue or even a clog; many are edible when they are young, but the majority of the species, because of their leathery, corky or woody consistency, are absolutely uneatable.

Perhaps the most prominent of the edible polypori is the Beef-Steak Fungus (*Fistulina heptica*), which can reach a considerable size (four to twelve inches in diameter). It is a beautiful blood red in colour, with a sticky surface and pink-veined skin; the pores, which are on the lower part, are pale ochre, but become covered with red-brown specks after being touched.

Polyporus pes-caprae has a very short stem and caps that fan outwards. These caps are thick and have a white skin, and their slightly scaly surface is velvety and coffee

Fungus of the craterellus type: its shape is trumpet-like, with longitudinal folds on the outside.

Fungus of the boletus type: the lower part of the cap is covered with countless pores, the openings of the spore-producing tubes.

coloured. The pores are yellowish white. It is an excellent autumn mushroom, characteristic of moorlands.

The caps of the Dryad's Saddle (*Polyporus* or *Poliporellus squamosus*) can reach 20 cm (8 in) in diameter. They are light in colour, and a few large brown scales cover the upper part; it makes good eating only when it is young, and its firm flesh smells of acid flour.

P. frondosus, which grows near stumps of underwood, has a characteristic scent and cluster. Its small, thin, fanned-out caps, which are often lobed or split, are brown grey in colour. This species is edible, and is found in summer in damp woods.

This survey of fungi is necessarily limited, but it must include those found most commonly in the woods in autumn.

The Hedgehog Fungus (*Hydnum repandum*), although tasty, is a little indigestible. It is distinguishable by the presence of many close-set prickles under the cap. The species of *Clavaria* are less advisable because of the bitter and resinous substances they contain, which can upset the digestive system.

There are various forms of *Clavariae*, from *Clavaria pistillaris*, a fleshy mass, thick at the top, to the strangest looking clusters or corollae, sometimes yellow (*C. aurea, C. flava*), sometimes pink (*C. botrytis*). The latter species is the only one which can be considered at all edible.

Puff-balls (species of *Lycoperdon*), are usually rounded, white or brownish, and found in meadows and mountain pastures. These fungi are little appreciated, but they are, in the majority of cases, non-poisonous. They are eaten when young, as their fructiferous body, on ripening, is reduced to a powdery mass of spores. When puff-balls burst, these millions of brown or black spores can cause respiratory irritation.

Phallus species and *Clathrus cancellatus* are strange phenomena in the world of fungi. Both are characterised by a strong smell: the fetid smell of tainted meat. They both grow on manure-heaps, which are rich in organic substances. *Phallus impudicus* is reminiscent of the morel because of its conical cap from which flows a thick,

greenish, putrid-smelling liquid containing the spores. *Clathrus cancellatus*, once it is completely developed, has a large, red, reticulated body. In the cavity of this body the spore-containing liquid flows between the speckles: this liquid is called *gleba*. Both of these, as well as the puff-balls, belong to the *Gasteromycetes*. Furthermore, they both develop from a sort of egg, leaving an irregularly torn volva at the base.

Morels, which have been mentioned above, belong to the *Ascomycetes*, unlike all the other fungi mentioned. They belong to the genus *Morchella*, and are spring fungi which grow in clayey or, less often, in chalky woods. Their cap, which can be rounded or conical (*mitre*), ochre, yellow, grey or brown, is always pitted with small cavities.

It is safe to say that all the morels are edible, and neighbouring genera like *Mitraphora* and *Verpa* are edible as well, although they are less appreciated. The inedible *Gyomitra* (for example *G. esculenta*) are not true morels.

It is appropriate to end a discussion on fungi types with truffles, those delicious underground fungi of the genus *Tuber*. Truffles are also *Ascomycetes*, and are extracted from the ground of oak and other plantations. Although they are difficult to find, truffles are one of the most sought-after of foodstuffs. There is a large number of species, but few are really good, and only two outstanding: the white truffle (*Tuber magnatum*) and the black truffle (*T. melanosporum*). A cut shows that the flesh is light grey in the first, and black brown in the second; in both cases this flesh is covered with a network of lighter veins, and this tangle contains the numerous round, verrucous and reticulated asci which in turn contain the large spores.

The deadly poisons

Anyone who intends to progress, from observing and studying fungi to eating them, clearly must have an exact knowledge of the species encountered. It is just as

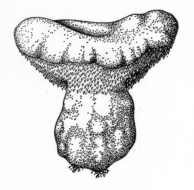

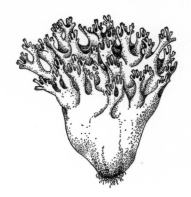

Fungus of the hydnum type: the lower part of the cap bears a great many fragile spines.

Fungus of the clavaria type: the upper part of the fruiting body is forked, each fork ending in a fertile tip.

obvious that the simplest method of determining whether a fungus is edible or poisonous – namely by sampling it – is totally impractical. Indeed, many traditional methods for testing fungi are unreliable, and should be noted.

The test of the bread-crumb, of the clove of garlic, of the coin or the small silver spoon are utterly worthless. Likewise, feeding doubtful specimens to a dog or cat is not only cruel, but often useless: the reaction may be different, or simply slower with these animals.

Further, it is dangerous to believe that fungi which have been nibbled by slugs or larvae are not poisonous. On the contrary, they can be very dangerous indeed. Not only the Fly Agaric, but also the terrible Death Cap, can often be found nibbled by fungi-eating creatures.

On the other hand, it is quite wrong to decide that fungi are poisonous on the sole grounds that they are close to an animal corpse, in the vicinity of a certain tree and so forth. Fungi simply are, or are not, poisonous, and this depends entirely on the species. Sometimes it may be that their toxicity is more accentuated in certain areas, but these variations are so exceptional and so slight that they should be ignored. All species of poisonous fungi have their own particular poisons, but this account is limited to *Amanita* and *Phallus* toxins.

There is a distinction made between 'real' poisonous fungi and those which have become poisonous as a result of damage or deterioration. Frost, for example, can make the most edible fungi dangerous. And ptomaine poisons – similar to those produced by the putrefaction of food in general – will occur in over-ripe fungi.

The most serious of all fungus poisoning is, without any doubt, that caused by *Amanita phalloides*, which in the majority of supervised cases proves fatal. This high mortality rate is due in part to the fact that the symptoms of poisoning do not appear until 12 to 48 hours after ingestion. By that time, the poison has reached the organs which are particularly vulnerable, namely the liver, heart, lungs and kidneys. The extent of the damage naturally depends upon the quantity of fungi ingested, but it also depends upon individual resistance.

When they do appear, the symptoms are alarming: violent abdominal pains, vomiting and a fetid diarrhea. This is followed by a period of calm, but it is only a false improvement, and is in turn followed by a repeated spell of the first symptoms, usually less intense. At the same time the patient suffers a collapse, during which his pulse weakens as it accelerates; his sight troubles him, but he never loses consciousness. Following the serious degeneration suffered by the liver and the red blood corpuscles, the condition inevitably becomes worse. In most cases the state of the patient becomes more and more critical, ending with death.

Other fungus poisonings are usually less serious. In the main, the toxin attacks the alimentary canal, resulting in vomiting, diarrhea and almost immediate visceral pains. Perspiration, headaches, tremblings and a feeling of exhaustion are often simultaneous symptoms. Finally, many fungi are only mildly toxic, and their effect is limited to the peculiar phenomena of ebriety and hallucination.

In search of fungi

It has already been mentioned that meadows and woods are the natural habitat of most species of fungi. Those which grow in woods are linked by symbiosis with a particular species of tree. Thus, each type of woodland has its complement of fungi.

Three kinds of wood: coniferous; beech; or woods composed of oaks, elms, hazels, chestnuts and maples are the most favourable for mycologists.

When a species of conifer such as the Scotch fir, *Picea* or larch forms a cool and rich forest with a mossy undergrowth, it is accompanied by characteristic fungi.

In larch woods, we find certain boleti including *Boletus elegans*, to which we can add *B. cavipes*; the latter is not highly rated because of the spongy mass of its pores.

In pine woods, *Boletus luteus* is found, and also *B. granulatus*, which has the upper part of its stem slightly granular. These boleti, like those to be found in larch woods, have a sticky cap. It is recommended that one remove the film which covers them, as this sticky skin is absolutely indigestible.

The red fir wood is amongst the richest in fungi. The boleti we have been speaking of are to be found there, especially when there are larches and pines, which is often the case. Boleti, lactarii and russulas are all found there. So is the plentiful chanterelle (*Cantharellus cibarius*), which makes an excellent condiment.

Obviously these woods also contain some poisonous species: the amanitas, especially if there are the necessary symbiotic plants. A few birch trees are sufficient for the Fly Agaric to decorate the woods plentifully with its red caps speckled with white. It is generally sufficient for a large beech, a poplar, a hazel or a chestnut to be hidden behind the dark foliage of the firs and the pine trees, for the panoply of fungi to offer an unforeseen variety of forms and colours.

Beech woods often shelter those dark-capped boleti which are safest for the novice. The woods we have spoken about also shelter tricholomas and amanitas, lepiotas and species of *Clitocybe*, which must be used with great caution.

The fungi living in the mixed woods are varied. The clavarias are very numerous; the Fairy Ring Champignon (*Marasmius oreades*) may be very common, together with the russulas, clavarias and, on the chestnuts, the polypores including the glowing Beef-Steak Fungus.

Certain fungi prefer the less humid, warmer and drier atmosphere of the oak woods: this is the case with the edible Orange-milk Agaric. In other woods, near each group of trees grow a variety of characteristic species.

Many fungi are also found in fields, where they live off dead matter such as manure. Fungi found here include the field mushrooms and the coprini. The lepiotas are also found in great numbers here (*Lepiota excoriata, L. naucina*) and, under very damp conditions, numerous small water fungi also grow, but these are unsuitable for cultivation.

Cultivated mushrooms

The delicate and often complicated connection between fungi and the medium in which they grow makes organised cultivation difficult, and in many cases impossible. Some saprophytic species of little food value (*Coprinus, Volvaria, Lepiota*) could be cultivated, but the Field Mushroom (*Agaricus campestris*) almost alone is exploited on a large scale.

The technique of growing field mushrooms – or cultivated mushrooms as they are usually called – lies in injecting the mycelium into a substratum as similar as possible to the natural substratum; for example smoked field compost. After a certain period of incubation, the mycelium starts to spread in the form of whitish filaments. About one month after inoculation the whitish and rounded rough shapes of fruiting bodies appear. The entire process may last for 4 to 5 months.

In the traditional method, old arcades, cellars, tunnels and caves are used, but it is not necessary to go underground: huts, greenhouses and garages are eminently suitable for the intensive technique by which beds are placed one on top of the other.

In fact, the type of place chosen is relatively unimportant. What is essential to success is the ability to provide the necessary humidity and a suitable organic substratum, free from dangerous parasites; in other words, to reconstruct the conditions under which field mushrooms flourish in nature.

Eating mushrooms

The nutritive value of mushrooms is negligible: they are made up of more than 90 per cent water, less than 3 per cent protein and less than 5 per cent carbohydrate. Nevertheless, they are an agreeable addition to the diet, with a delicate flavour and a pleasant consistency; some, such as the parasol mushroom (*Lepiota procera*), are often tastier than the cultivated or field mushroom. Other varieties, such as the beefsteak fungus, are so distinctive in appearance that they are easily identified. But there are a number of very poisonous fungi which can readily be mistaken for the edible mushroom, and it is worth studying the characteristics of these species very closely.

Poisoning by mushrooms can be fatal, or it can produce only a mild gastrointestinal disturbance or the symptoms of mild allergy. No doubt the most dangerous are three species of the *Amanita* genus: *A. phalloides*, *A. verna* and *A. virosa*. These can occur abundantly in mushroom-gathering areas, and novices should take great care to study and observe the specimens they gather on several occasions before they sample them as food. The illustrations on the following pages should serve as an additional guide to the identification of the most poisonous species.

Page 13: (above) *Amanita panterina*; (below) *A. muscaria*
Page 14: *A. phalloides*
Page 15: (above) *A. virosa*; (below) *A. verna*

Index to illustrations

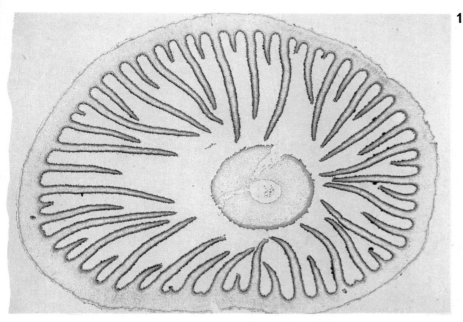

1 This is a horizontal section of a field mushroom cap, with the stalk showing in the centre. The gills can be seen radiating from the edge of the cap, and on their rough outer surfaces the dark granular layer of spore-producing cells (basidia) is visible.

2 *Amanita caesarea* is the only species of *Amanita* which has gills, a stem and a ring in beautiful yellow. It is an edible mushroom and very much sought-after in leafy woods with a mild temperature. Although it is easily identifiable, it is sometimes confused with the very poisonous Death Cap (*A. phalloides*) which has white parts. *A. caesarea* is also closely related to the Fly Agaric (*A. muscaria*) which, like *A. phalloides*, has white gills but is distinguished by a red cap speckled with white warts (plates 6–8).

3 The Death Cap (*Amanita phalloides*) is without doubt the fungus to which may be attributed most fatal poisonings. The two examples photographed above show its characteristics: a cap almost olive green in colour; close, white gills; a ring and volva which are both equally white. This fungus is especially dangerous when it is very young and still enclosed in the volva (having an egg-like shape). This is why it is better not to gather any *Amanita* species when they are too young, as the colour of their cap is not sufficiently clear to avoid possibly fatal confusions.

4

5

4-5 Two more deadly amanitas: *Amanita verna* and *A. virosa*. *A. verna* may be considered as the completely white variety of the Death Cap, as it has the same external characteristics. *A. virosa* differs from it on account of its cap, which is convex and has nipples on it instead of being flat. Its three constant characteristics, gills which are always white, the ring and the volva, should prevent any confusion with the edible mushrooms with a white cap. When the two species which we have just quoted, like the Death Cap, have the form of an egg, the pointed part is turned upwards, whereas in *A. caesarea* it is turned downwards (sketch below).

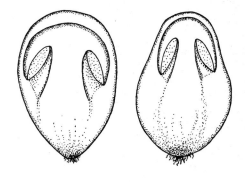

6-7 An orange-red or vermilion cap, speckled with white warts, and a stem and a ring which are both very white, make the Fly Agaric (*Amanita muscaria*) the most remarkable of the numerous fungi which grow in autumn in woods and on moors. This attractive appearance is deceptive, however. In fact, although it is not as dangerous as the Death Cap, it is poisonous. Sometimes it may be confused with the Orange-milk Agaric (*A. caesarea*) which, however, has no white warts on its cap and whose gills, ring and stem are yellow. From the sketch it can be seen that the volva has characteristic wart-like bulges.

7

6

8 A species related to *Amanita muscaria* is *A. aureola*, which does not have any warts on its cap. This, too, might be confused with the Orange-milk Agaric except that its stem, gills and ring are white. It is as poisonous as the Fly Agaric.

9-10 The appearance of the Panther Cap, *Amanita pantherina*, is characteristic because of the brown cap speckled with white warts. The presence of a striated edge to its cap enables this poisonous fungus to be distinguished from the Blusher (*A. rubescens*) pictured below, which resembles it because of its chestnut-brown colour. The Panther Cap is very poisonous, whereas the Blusher is edible, except when uncooked.

9

10

11

11 Three examples of *Amanita citrina*, at various stages of growth. A cylindrical stem and a convex and flattened pale citrine cap emerge from a spherical body. Although it is not really poisonous, it is inedible.

12-13 *Amanitopsis vaginata* differs from the true amanitas by the absence of a ring, although it has a volva. The striated edge to its cap always allows it to be distinguished from the Death Cap, in spite of the fact that some varieties of *A. vaginata* have a similar colour. Other varieties of this species are variously coloured in grey, brick red or shades of brown. This fungus is edible but little appreciated.

12

13

14

14-15 The Parasol Mushroom, *Lepiota procera*, is one of the most easily recognised fungi. One of the illustrations show a fungus which has only recently burst open; the other, a fungus whose cap still adheres, in characteristic fashion, to the ring. The mobile ring and the white gills are clearly visible in plate 14. It is a fungus which is commonly found towards the end of summer and during the entire autumn, in leafy, cool woods. It is edible, but must not be eaten when it is too far developed as its hard and fibrous stem is particularly indigestible. As the sketch shows, when the fungus is fully developed the cap flattens out, retaining a nipple and a scaly appearance.

16

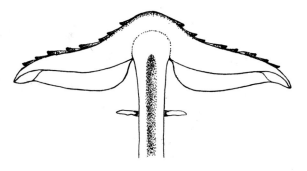

16 Similar to *Lepiota procera*, but generally smaller, *L. exoriata* has a much less scaly cap whose outer layer is broken into silky patches. The two species, as the sketch shows, have free gills. They are both edible.

17 *Lepiota naucina* has pink gills. Very small, its maximum height is scarcely 10 cm (4 in). Its white or whitish cap often cracks under the action of the wind. It is an edible fungus which is sometimes found in great quantity in fields, meadows, pastures and even kitchen gardens, from summer through autumn.

15

17

18

19

20

18 Two examples of one of the smallest species of the genus *Lepiota*, *L. helveola*, which is poisonous, like many small fungi.

19 *Lepiota nympharum* has a cap covered with numerous irregular scales which hang over the edge and give the whole fungus a tattooed appearance. From the culinary point of view it is a dubious species.

20 Here is one of the rare lepiotas whose cap does not scale off, but is extremely rough. This fungus, *Lepiota Friesii*, is not edible because of the acid and very disagreeable smell it produces.

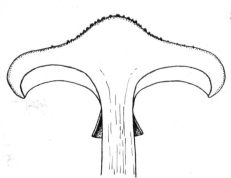

21   A cluster of *Armillaria mellea*, each of which has a scaly cap which is brown in the centre. These are autumn fungi, parasites of numerous species of plants, whose colour varies according to the species on which they grow. These fungi are edible, but can become dangerous when they suffer weathering due to rain and frost. *A. mellea* can be preserved in vinegar or oil, and is the last fungus to be collected before winter sets in. The sketch shows the gills completely inserted in the stem, and slightly decurrent (extending down along the stem).

22   Three examples of the same species of fungi, where the ring is very clearly turned downwards.

21

22

23 Examples of *Armillaria imperialis* at different stages of growth. These are fungi of a remarkable size, with a fawn-chestnut cap which remains closed for a long time. In the undergrowth they can be taken for the commonly eaten mushrooms, but the ring (see the sketch below) and the gills are both characteristics which leave no doubt. It is not a poisonous fungus but is distinguished by its slightly bitter smell which it keeps even after cooking. The sketch shows the characteristic 'sock', which encloses the stem and constitutes, to some extent, a double ring.

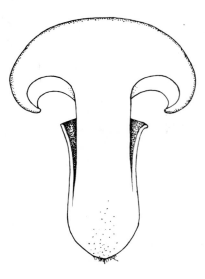

24

24-5 Because of its gills and ochre-grey cap, the harmless *Clitocybe nebularis* (plate 24) can be confused with the poisonous *Entoloma sinuatus*. The poisonous *Clitocybe cerusata* (plate 25) bears a dangerous resemblance to the edible *Clitopilus prunulus*.

26 Here are four examples of *Clitocybe rivulosa*, one of the white clitocybes. These are very poisonous fungi which unfortunately can be confused with edible mushrooms.

25

26

27

28

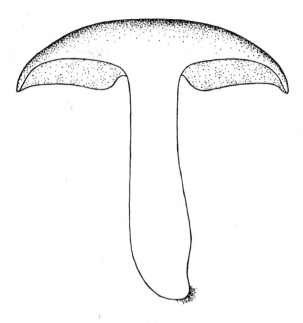

29 In *Tricholoma flavbrunneum* note the contrast between the yellow of the gills and the more or less dark reddish brown of the cap. Like most tricholomas it is not poisonous, although it emits a strong smell of flour and has rather a bitter taste. The sketch shows a closely related species, *T. albobrunneum*, which has the same characteristics.

30 Generally considered as a doubtful source of food, *Tricholoma vaccinum* has a cap almost identical in colour to that of *T. flavobrunneum*. However, it always has a central core and scales. Its disagreeable and slightly bitter flesh allows it to be distinguished from similar but edible species.

29

30

27 An agreeably and characteristically scented species, *Clitocybe geotrope* is a beautiful biscuit colour, and is often found growing in large irregular rings. It is an edible mushroom when young, and is appreciated for its scent, which is something like that of wild mint.

28 Living in large groups, *Tricholoma terreum* is an edible small fungus, with a dark grey cap covered in small scales. One must be very careful not to confuse it with *T. tigrinum* (= *T. pardinum*), a poisonous fungus which is slightly larger in size, more silvery grey, and has a finely scaled cap rather than a fibrous one. *T. terreum* is commonly called Grey Agaric.

31-2 The Narcissus Blewit (*Tricholoma sulphurum*, plate 31) is inedible because of the strong smell of gas which it produces. This distinguishes it clearly from a somewhat similar relative, the Firwood Agaric (*T. equestre*, plate 32), which is quite edible and produces no smell. Any remaining confusion between these two species is overcome by the fact that the former has yellowish flesh, as shown by cutting it, and the latter has white flesh, whose surface on the cap is sticky and covered in green-brown fibres.

31

33

34

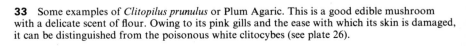

33 Some examples of *Clitopilus prunulus* or Plum Agaric. This is a good edible mushroom with a delicate scent of flour. Owing to its pink gills and the ease with which its skin is damaged, it can be distinguished from the poisonous white clitocybes (see plate 26).

34 Arranged in rows or circles, the Fairy Ring Champignon (*Marasmius oreades*) may cover grassy areas of meadows and woods. It is a small, edible fungus used as a condiment.

35 The Red-haired Agaric (*Tricholoma rutilans*) is a fungus admired above all for its purple-red, downy surface composed of small scales, which contrasts with the yellow background of the cap. It is edible.

36

37

38

36-7 These small species of fungi belong to the genus *Laccaria*. They are remarkable for the variety of their colours, which embrace the whole range of pinks, violets and lilacs. *L. amethystina*, is a beautiful deep violet (plate 36), while *L. laccata* has widely spaced gills and is pink violet in colour (plate 37). Both species are edible.

38 *Russula virescens* (the greenish russula) is identified by its cap, which is cracked and covered in numerous coloured warts. This is an edible fungus which is very much appreciated for its flavour.

39 Among the largest and least common species of hygrophori is *Hygrophorus Russula*. The examples illustrated show the wine-red patches on the cap and stem which are characteristic. Humidity makes it sticky, yet it is edible. Its white, slightly pink or stained flesh is sweet or slightly bitter at maturity. It is found in the middle of autumn under dead leaves.

39

40-1 The russulas are very tempting because of their bright colours, but they are not all equally edible. A curious trick of nature makes almost every edible *Russula* have a pungent and doubtful double. *R. emetica* (plate 40), which is bitter and slightly poisonous, and the very edible *R. lepida* both have a bright red cap, more crimson in *R. lepida*, which is startling against the whiteness of the gills and stem. The latter species is delicious but it must be boiled before being cooked any other way. It is possible to identify it when it is cooking by the smell of its flesh which is first sweet and then slightly bitter; by contrast, the flesh of *R. emetica* is very pungent. The sketch shows a section of *R. lepida* and shows the free gills which are inserted in the stem. The colour of the cap of the russulas varies greatly, and there are numerous species (plate 41) with shades going from red to violet.

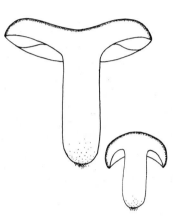

40

41

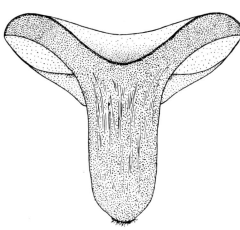

42-3 Here we have two scarcely attractive russulas: *Russula nigricans* (plate 42) with thick, widely-spaced gills, which turn red as soon as they are touched and finally go as brown as the cap; and *R. foetens* (plate 43) which is characterised by a nauseating smell which makes it inedible. These are the two most characteristic species of russulas. They are found, generally, in great numbers in autumn in beech and oak woods and on heaths. *R. nigricans* reaches considerable dimensions and its cap, as the sketch shows, is depressed in the centre.

44

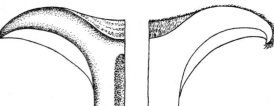

44 The Saffron Milk Cap (*Lactarius deliciosus*), which is found in pine woods as early as the end of summer and until very late in autumn, can be confused with the Woolly Milk Cap (*L. torminosus*, plate 45). The former species is held in high esteem even though its unattractive appearance, especially when it is covered with dirty green spots, sometimes repels those who are not familiar with it. The sketch shows clearly the difference between the two caps (edible species on the left, poisonous on the right).

45 *Lactarius torminosus*: its milk is white, it does not bend and the surface of its cap is covered with a characteristic down, more visible on the edge. It can cause quite serious gastro-intestinal troubles.

46 Another species of *Lactarius* which is not edible. This is *L. scrobiculatus*, easily recognisable by its yellowish cap and its stem decorated with very visible dimples. Its white milk yellows when exposed to the air. All the *Lactarius* species with milk that is initially colourless should be avoided, even if they are not known to be really poisonous fungi.

46

47

47 *Lactarius vellereus* is a large white fungus which is frequently found, summer and autumn, in woods. Its widely-spaced ochre or almost white gills and its velvety cap should be sufficient to distinguish it from similar species, which also have a bitter and peppery taste.

48 An adult example of *Lactarius controversus*, a very bitter, large and robust fungus. The spaced-out gills are of a pale skin-pink colour, which distinguishes this species from *L. piperatus* (plate 50), whose white gills are close together.

48

50

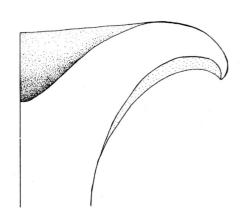

49 Similar to the lactarii in its appearance and its slightly decurrent and uneven gills, *Russula delica* does not have any milk. This is an edible species which is found in woods.

50 Lower part of the cap of *Lactarius piperatus*: the gills are very close and slightly decurrent. It is very bitter, and this is why, in certain regions, when it has been dried and ground it is substituted for pepper. In the sketch the depression in the cap, and the very close gills, can be clearly seen.

51

51 *Gomphidius viscidus* is frequently found in autumn, especially in coniferous woods. It is copper red in colour, with a slightly nippled cap, a cylindrical, elongated stem and rather decurrent gills. All *Gomphidius* species are edible.

52 Groups of very ruddy fungi are sometimes found among moss. They must be avoided, especially if their species cannot be clearly identified; this is all the more difficult when they are very young fungi.

53-4 It is a commonly held belief that fungi in clusters are edible. However, the species of the genus *Hypholoma*, which grow in large clusters, are often poisonous. They differ from other similar groups in the absence of a persistent ring and the colour of their gills. Plate 53: *H. capnoides*, yellowish grey in colour, sweetish in flavour and non-poisonous. Plate 54: *H. sublateritium* has a deep brick-red cap and livid yellow gills; it has a bitter, disagreeable flavour.

52

53

55 *Cortinarius praestans* is a stout fungus with a purplish-brown convex cap and a bulbous, whitish stem. It has firm, soapy and almost odourless flesh, and is perhaps the only species of the genus *Cortinarius* that is universally considered edible. It is found quite frequently in autumn in oak woods.

56

56 *Cortinarius fulmineus*, which has a yellow stem and gills, belongs to a large group of cortinarii which are very brightly coloured. This species, which is often found in woods, has no great edible value although it is not dangerous.

57 *Cortinarius collinitus* is characterised by two main features: its extreme stickiness, which deters people from collecting it, although it is not poisonous; and the rows of scales which cover the stem. The feature which gives the cortinarii their name is the cortine, a silky veil which links the edge of the cap to the stem. This is clearly shown in the accompanying sketch and also in the right-hand specimen in plate 57 as a bluish-white gore underneath the developing cap.

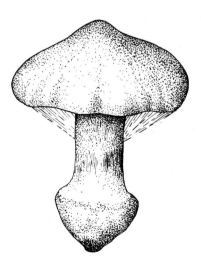

57

58

58 The cortine, broken by expansion of the maturing cap, often remains on the top part of the stem, as in the case of these examples of *Cortinarius aurantioturbinatus*, where it takes the form of an irregular ring which shows up brown when the spores are released.

59 One of the most common cortinarii in the woods: *Cortinarius albo-violaceus*, which is lilac white in colour, and shows the development and structure of the cortine very clearly. Both this species and the one above are inoffensive, but are not recommended.

59

60

60   This is another *Cortinarius* (*C. variegatus*). The variety of species in this genus is such that their identification is often very difficult, even for those who specialise in them.

61   A typical woodland and edible species, *Pluteus cervinus* is certainly the most common of the genus *Pluteus*. When the convex cap is ripped, the well-spaced gills are seen to be coloured pink. This feature is shared by another genus, *Entoloma*.

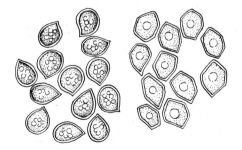

62 The psalliotas always have coloured gills: pink when they are young, purplish blue or purplish brown when they have reached the adult stage. The colour is due to the spores formed on the gills. The three examples of *Agaricus arvensis* in the illustration reflect clearly the progressive development of the spores, as little by little the colour of the gills darkens. One must be careful not to use in cooking those psalliotas which are slender in form and whose flesh, on being touched, becomes sulphur yellow immediately: this is *A. xanthoderma*, which is slightly poisonous. *A. arvensis*, the largest of the psalliotas, is the best known of the edible fungi, though few people today have experienced the superb taste of the wild mushroom; the mushrooms raised commercially are cultivated varieties derived from it. Care must be taken not to confuse it with the white amanitas, to which *Amanita phalloides* belongs. The psalliotas are recognisable by their volva and their pink or purple – but never white – gills.

63

65

64

63-4 The coprini, or ink caps, are short-lived fungi which are easily recognised. The illustration shows two stages of development of a group of *Coprinus picaceus* (above) and *C. micaceus* (below). When young, they are enclosed in an ellipsoid cap, sometimes covered with large white scales. At this stage their shape is rather like that of small clubs. They then develop into a stalk and a conical cap. These fungi are practically harmless, but these two species do not have any food value. They also produce a particularly disagreeable odour.

65 Two young and small specimens of *Coprinus*. It is advisable to leave these small fungi alone.

66-7 Young specimens of *Coprinus comatus* (Shaggy Ink Cap) photographed at the only stage at which they can be eaten. One of the two specimens on the right will soon dissolve into a mass of black spores: this is indicated by its widely conical cap which is turning black. These coprini are harmful if they are consumed when they are too old, especially if wine or any other alcoholic drink is taken at the same time. Generally speaking, the coprini are delicate, watery fungi, with many species being small in size and fragile in structure (see sketch below).

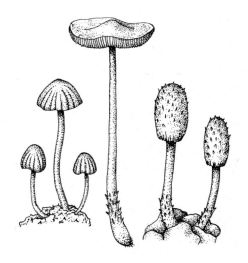

68

69

68 The Chanterelle, *Cantharellus cibarius*, very well known and much appreciated for its delicate and fruity perfume, is clearly recognisable by its yellow colour. Nevertheless, inexpert collectors can confuse them with *Clitocybe clearia*. The latter, however, grows in clusters, and its flesh is bright yellow and not near white.

69 Detail of the gills of a chanterelle; they are more like small veins or pronounced folds which fuse and split in an irregular pattern.

70

70 The long, orange-coloured stem of *Cantharellus lutescens* contrasts with its dark-brown scaly cap. Although edible this species is less appreciated than *C. cibarius*.

71 The Horn of Plenty (*Craterellus cornucopioides*) is an edible species consisting of irregular funnels with crinkled edges. Its unattractive appearance is compensated for by its sweet and fruity smell. The accompanying sketch gives some idea of the simple structure of this fungus.

71

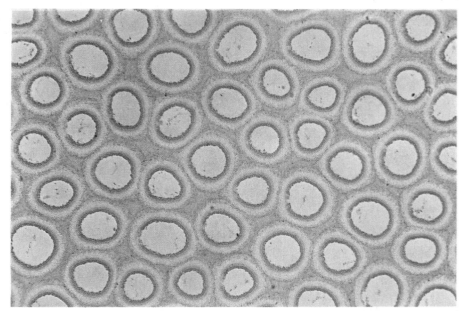

72 The boleti are very well-known fungi. The gills are replaced by tubes which form a spongy mass on the lower part of the cap, the colour of which may be white, yellow, green, red or orange. Here is a stained transverse section of some tubes belonging to a *Boletus*: each tube is lined with a darkly-stained fertile layer (the hymenium) which produces the spores.

73 One of the most sought-after fungi, the Cep (*Boletus edulis*), is distinguished from other *Boletus* species by the flesh, which retains its white colour even after breaking. The upper part of the stem is characterised by a finely stippled surface.

74

74 *Boletus edulis* var. *aereus* is held in even greater esteem than *B. edulis* itself. This is a variety of cep with a darker cap, whose pores remain white longer. It grows in beech and chestnut woods and is chosen for its hard and crisp flesh, which is particularly agreeable.

75 *Boletus edulis* var. *pinicola* also belongs to the cep group. It is found in coniferous woods but also under leaves from spring to autumn. It has a red cap which is usually a little damp and sticky. Its flesh is reddish white under the cap.

75

76 In *Boletus edulis* var. *pinicola*, two examples of which are shown in the illustration, the pores verge on yellow, even in the young fungi. The reddish colour of the cap is sometimes found in the stalk as well.

56

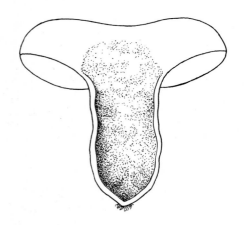

77

78

79

77 *Boletus castaneus*, which is not very common, has a cinnamon-coloured cap and a hollow stalk. The bed of tubes is pierced with very small, round, white pores which later turn pale yellow. This is an edible fungus tasting of hazel-nuts, with flesh that remains white with storage.

78 Three examples of *Boletus subtomentosus*, which is not very tasty. This is an autumn fungus found in woods. It has a brown cap, while its yellowish flesh sometimes turns blue green quickly, on contact with the air.

79 *Boletus chrysenteron* is edible, but not very tasty. Just underneath the skin of its cap it has a characteristic crimson-red colour. Its rather large pores are olive yellow and after a time turn greenish brown. These characteristics distinguish it from *B. subtomentosus* (plate 78).

80 The noteworthy features of the beautiful *Boletus rufus* are the brick-red cap and the blackish speckles on the stalk. Its white flesh changes colour on cooking, eventually becoming black, a process which is sometimes said – wrongly – to indicate a poisonous fungus; this species is perfectly edible. A related species, *B. scaber* (= *Trachypus carpini*), is also edible, but it is distinguished from *B. rufus* by a more slender stalk and a brownish-grey cap.

80

81

81 *Boletus Boudieri*, which is harmless, is comparatively difficult to find. This is a species clearly characterised by its colour and its stalk, which is speckled with numerous dark red scales.

82 The pores of *Boletus luteus* are protected in the young fungus by a purplish veil. By contrast, the sticky cap, which can be easily detached, has a brown covering. The slightly yellow flesh is thick and quite tasty. The sketch below shows that the closely related *B. granulatus* does not have any trace of a ring. In addition, the upper part of the stem is granular. Both species are edible.

82

83 Two examples of the characteristic golden-yellow colour of *Boletus elegans*. The partial veil remains on the upper part of the stem and forms a sort of persistent ring. The skin of the cap, which is sticky in damp weather, can be easily peeled and this operation makes the fungus less indigestible. The less savoury *B. viscidus* is a closely related species, though less attractive as its cap is even more sticky and pale grey in colour. They may often be found growing together.

84

85

86

86 *Boletus pachipus* is a very bitter, but non-poisonous, fungus. A characteristic web with light speckles is clearly outlined on a purple-red background, and decorates the upper half of the stalk. This fungus is frequently found in coniferous woods.

84 *Boletus tridentinus*, whose pores are orangy red, is a form closely related to *B. elegans* (plate 83). It is edible.

85 Beside the typically scaly cap of *Boletus cavipes*, if the fungus is turned over, its angular, irregular, large and slightly decurrent pores are clearly revealed. The remains of the ring can also be seen. The most distinguishing characteristic of this fungus is its completely hollow stalk. It should not be eaten.

87 Two examples of *Boletus luridus*. It is easily distinguished from the other species with red pores by the coarse red and brown web which decorates its yellowish stem. While some people consider it to be edible, this opinion is by no means universal.

88 *Boletus purpureus* is an edible species. It is greyish with the skin of the cap delicately shaded carmine. This fungus is the one which most clearly resembles *B. Satanus*, whose edible qualities are doubtful. The species are distinguished by the fact that *B. purpureus* has yellow flesh under the red stalk surface. Also, the pores, which are yellow at first, eventually turn a vivid red.

89

90

91

89 The poisonous *Boletus satanas* is characterised by a pale, greyish cap and blood-red pores, which together make it easy to identify. In addition, it has a delicate red network spread over the upper part of the stalk. The yellowish flesh quickly turns bluish when exposed to air.

90 Here is a peculiar bolete, *Strobilomyces strobilaceus*, a leathery fungus with dark scales on a white background and smoky-grey pores. It is not edible.

91 The cap of *Polyporellus squamosus* is remarkable for its size and its light-brown scales standing out on a pale, tobacco-coloured background. The penetrating smell of acid flour and the toughness of its flesh, especially when it is old, make it of little culinary value, although it is edible. The sketch shows a section of the cap.

92 Rigid and tough, the small fruiting bodies of *Coriolus versicolor* are sometimes arranged individually, sometimes partially fused, but are always decorated with zones of different colours. It is a species generally found on dead wood and on stumps. It belongs to the large group of fungi which are inedible because they are tough or corky.

93

93 Among the edible polypores, *Polyporus frondosus* is perhaps the most decorative. It appears in large clusters, subdivided into numerous branches of thin, minute brackets. Because of its firm, white flesh it is sometimes used with the Cep (*Boletus edulis*) in the preparation of *hors d'oeuvres*.

94

94 The fan-shaped caps of *Polyporus giganteus*. On the lower part of these caps countless white and rounded pores can be seen.

95 The large, fleshy, and blood-red fruiting body of *Fistulina hepatica* justifies its popular name: Beef-steak Fungus. It is an edible fungus when it is young, in spite of its stickiness. It often grows on old chestnut trees.

95

96   Although equipped with a stem and a cap, the hydnas, instead of having gills or pores, have spines on the lower part of their caps. The illustration is a transverse section of some of these spines in *Hydnum*.

97   *Hydnum repandum* is a conspicuous fungus whose yellow colour and large size allow it to be mistaken for a chanterelle. When turned upside-down, however, numerous pointed spines are immediately visible and these will prevent the confusion. It is edible.

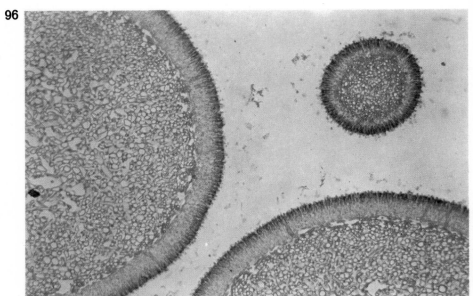

96

97

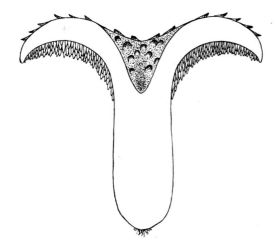

98 *Hydnum* spines are fragile and spread in an irregular pattern down the stalk. Although edible, it is best prepared in vinegar, as this eliminates its slightly bitter taste. The sketch shows the unusual structure of this fungus.

98

70

99 Here is a beautiful example of *Clavaria botrytis*, on which can clearly be distinguished the thick, fleshy and whitish base, and the short branches of the upper, fertile part. These characteristics allow it to be distinguished from the other clavarias that grow in clusters; such clavarias are generally dubious, but the species shown here is the least dangerous.

100 A close-up of the orange-coloured branches of *Clavaria formosa*, one of the most impressive clavarias.

99

100

101

102

103

104

101 A cluster of yellow *Clavaria flava*, which is frequently found in woods. It is best to avoid eating it.

102 Much smaller than the clavarias, *Calocera viscosa*, with its golden-yellow colour, contrasts strikingly with the surrounding vegetation.

103 The characteristic club-shaped fruiting bodies of *Clavaria pistillaris*. It is edible when young.

104 Often found in the autumn, among pine needles, are the tongue-shaped bodies of *Spathularia flavida*, supported by a small whitish stalk. These fungi are of little interest from the culinary point of view.

105 A section, seen through the microscope, of the fruiting body of a puff-ball (*Lycoperdon* species). Inside, the developing spores are seen as a brown mass.

106 The small puff-balls frequently found in the woods in autumn have an almost spherical form, and are covered with small warts similar to precious stones, from which they get their name: *Lycoperdon perlatum*. They are only edible when their flesh appears completely white and compact on breaking open.

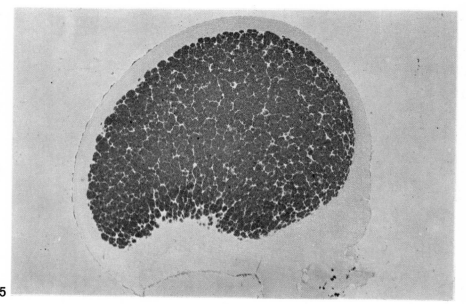

105

106

107

107 Long spines, fused at their tips into small groups, cover the surface of *Lycoperdon echinatum*.

108 One species of *Lycoperdon* can reach a considerable size: *L. giganteum*. The illustration shows an open, mature fruiting body in which the brown spores are exposed to the atmosphere for dispersal by wind and rain.

108

109 Like the puff-balls (*Lycoperdon*) with which they are easily confused, *Scleroderma* species are rounded, with no gills, pores or spines, but they have a thick, hard skin and are poisonous. The figure shows an example of *Scleroderma vulgare*. It is still closed, and its gnarled surface is covered with flattened warts. The sketch shows a section of a ripe *Scleroderma* in which the thickness of the outer skin can be seen.

110 Two mature specimens of the same species, of which one has split open at the top, revealing the spores.

111-12 Two curious examples of *Geaster rufescens*. It is an interesting fungus but it has no food value. Its external water-sensitive casing breaks open in the form of a star, in the centre of which stands the mass of spores.

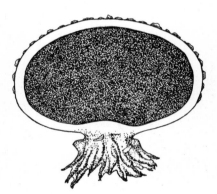

110

111

112

113 A longitudinal section of a very strange egg-shaped fungus: *Phallus impudicus*, very young stage.

114-15 The fungus has torn the gelatinous volva, showing clearly a cylindrical stalk crowned with a conical cap. This in turn is covered with a greenish mucilage, which is the liquid fertile layer and the spores, and which produces a repellent, putrid smell attractive to flies. This substance disappears and reveals the meshwork of the cap itself.

116 *Mutinus caninus* has an equally repellent smell. This is also found in woods.

113

114

115

116

117-18 Two examples of *Helvella crispa*, with a typically ribbed stem and undulating, lobed cap covered by the fertile layer.

119 *Helvella monachella* is a fungus which appears in spring. Its cap is dark and can even be black. It is an edible fungus; nevertheless, it must be used warily due to the acid which it produces.

117

118

119

120 These fungi, known as the *Pezizae*, have a fruiting body which takes the shape of a cup or even an ear. The inner surface of the cup is lined by the fertile layer which, in this example of *P. repanda*, is chocolate brown in colour.

121 The morels, like the pezizas, are *Ascomycetes*. These are edible, spring fungi whose mitre-shaped caps are hollowed out into a meshwork. The stalk is hollow. The earliest and most common of the morels is *Morchella vulgaris*. The morels with a yellow-ochre cap are also very much sought-after (*M. rotunda* and *M. esculenta*): they both grow in poplar woods and sparse, grassy and sandy woods. The sketch shows a related form, *Gyomitra esculenta*, whose edible qualities are doubtful.

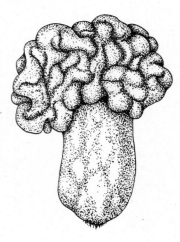

122

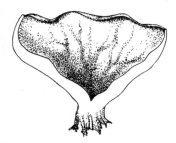

122 Some cups of *Peziza umbrina*, which are fragile in appearance. The fertile layer is dark brown. They are found among the moss and lichens of the undergrowth. One must be wary of these curious, small fungi. The sketch shows a section of the fruiting body of a *Peziza*.

123 A species closely related to that in plate 122. Its colour is striking, going from bright yellow to vivid red.

123

125

124

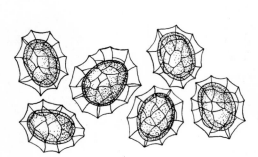

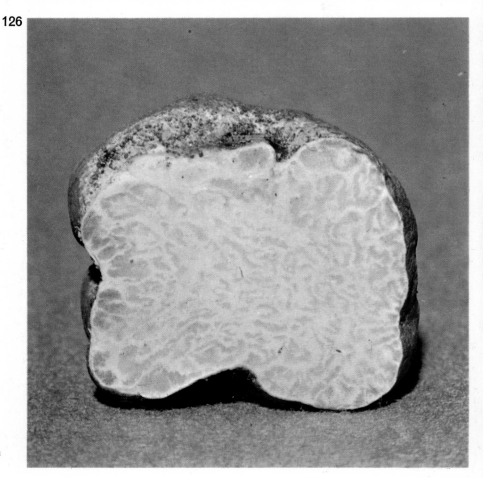

126

124 *Tuber melanosporum* is a truffle. These are subterranean fungi which require experience in knowing where to unearth them. They are rare, but often locally abundant.

125-6 *Tuber magnatum* has much more taste and value than has *T. melanosporum*. The photographs show a whole fruiting body and a section. The flesh appears clearly mottled. The sketch shows the characteristic spores of this truffle.